THE BIBLE *and the* SACRAMENTS

PARTICIPANT WORKBOOK

ST. PAUL CENTER
FOR BIBLICAL THEOLOGY

JOURNEY THROUGH SCRIPTURE

Writers: Matthew Leonard, Raquel Lopez, Emily Stimpson, David Scott, Mike Aquilina
Media/Print Production: Matthew Leonard, Raquel Lopez, Patty Borgman, Scionka INC, Lannette Turicchi, Alex Renn
Graphic Design: Patty Borgman

Acknowledgement: We sincerely thank all those whose generosity of time, talent and finances made this project possible. Of special note are Betsy Orr & Family, and Ernest P. Waud III in loving memory of his wife Marilyn M. Waud

St. Paul Center for Biblical Theology
1468 Parkview Circle
Steubenville, OH 43952

Front Cover image: *The Baptism of Christ* – Antoine Coypel
Photo Credit: Restored Traditions

Table of Contents

❧❧❧❧

Welcome to Journey Through Scripture

Journey Through Scripture is the St. Paul Center's dynamic Bible study program designed to help ordinary Catholics grow in their knowledge of Scripture while deepening their understanding of the riches of our faith. Distinctively Catholic, Journey Through Scripture reads the Bible from the heart of the Church, considering both the Old and New Testaments and how they work together. It's grounded in history, yet actively engages topics faced by today's Catholics. More than just an ordinary Bible study, it's biblical catechesis.

There are several Journey Through Scripture studies. This participant workbook is for *The Bible and the Sacraments*, a dynamic eleven-part video series that examines the sacraments of the Catholic faith. Exploring their meaning and origin, *The Bible and the Sacraments* investigates the deeper mysteries they contain as illuminated by Sacred Scripture.

After presenting two overview lessons, *The Bible and the Sacraments* explores each sacrament individually. It examines where the sacraments come from, what they mean, and why they are so foundational to our faith.

STUDY COMPONENTS

The Bible and the Sacraments is designed for both group and individual study. It contains five possible components, all of which can be ordered at **BibleandtheSacraments.com**.

- This participant workbook

- *The Bible and the Sacraments* leader guide

- *The Bible and the Sacraments* DVD set

- *Swear to God: The Promise and Power of the Sacraments* by Dr. Scott Hahn

- *Speaking the Love of God: An Introduction to the Sacraments* by Jacob Wood

Lesson One
INTRODUCTION *to the* MYSTERIES

"Sacraments are 'powers that come forth' from the Body of Christ, which is ever-living and life-giving. They are actions of the Holy Spirit at work in his Body, the Church. They are 'the masterworks of God' in the new and everlasting covenant."

CCC 1116

Introduction *to the* Mysteries

In paragraph 1116, the *Catechism of the Catholic Church* describes the sacraments as "'the masterworks of God' in the new and everlasting covenant." More than mere earthly rituals, they are "'powers that come forth' from the Body of Christ, which is ever-living and life-giving."

The Bible and the Sacraments dives into the mystery of these God-given channels of grace. It illuminates the deeply scriptural roots of the sacraments, examining the rich relationship between the Old and New Testaments and their connection to the rites of the Catholic Church.

What we'll discover throughout this study is that the sacraments we celebrate are nothing new. God has always dealt with humanity in a sacramental manner. Finding their institution in Christ and their origin in salvation history, Baptism, Confirmation, the Eucharist, Penance, Anointing of the Sick, Marriage, and Holy Orders are God's gifts of life and love to his children.

☺ What We'll Cover in Lesson One

INTRODUCTION

Matthew Leonard, Vice President of the St. Paul Center and host of the series

THEMES COVERED

❧ The many levels of meaning of the sacraments

❧ How the sacraments of grace are efficacious "signs"

❧ The role of "sacraments" in the Old Testament

❧ The purpose and power of typology

❧ The three stages of salvation history

❧ How the sacraments make us children of God

SCRIPTURE VERSES READ BY CARDINAL DONALD WUERL IN THIS LESSON

❧ Matthew 28:18–20

❧ Colossians 2:11–12

Notes

Sacrament Outward sign instastuted by Christ

Signs - Visible

Typology -

"*The sacraments of the New Testament give salvation, the sacraments of the Old Testament promise a savior.*"

— *St. Augustine* —

Review Questions

1. How are signs and sacraments similar? How are they different?

2. What is typology? Why is it important?

3. What are the three stages of salvation history? Why are they important to understanding the sacraments of grace?

4. What are some examples of Old Testament "sacraments"? What did Christ do with them?

Discussion Questions

1. What do sacraments tell us about the place of the physical matter, creation, in God's plan?

2. What does it mean to live "sacramental" lives?

THIS LESSON'S MEMORY VERSE

"Go therefore and make disciples of all nations, baptizing them in the name of the Father and of the Son and of the Holy Spirit, teaching them to observe all that I have commanded you; and behold, I am with you always, to the end of the age."
— *Matthew 28:19–20* —

FOLLOW-UP READING AND PREPARATION FOR THE NEXT LESSON

- *Swear to God* by Scott Hahn, pp. 2–23

- *Speaking the Love of God* by Jacob Wood, pp. 1–16

- *Catechism of the Catholic Church*, paragraphs 1077–1112

Additional study resources can be found at www.StPaulCenter.com

Lesson Two
The RITUAL of FAMILY

"Liturgical catechesis aims to initiate people into the mystery of Christ (It is 'mystagogy.') by proceeding from the visible to the invisible, from the sign to the thing signified, from the 'sacraments' to the 'mysteries'."

CCC 1075

Review of the Previous Lesson

Jesus became flesh and blood in order to heal our flesh and blood. But his healing of humanity is more than physical. He brings us spiritual healing and salvation. To perform these spiritual healings, Jesus used physical means because he knows that as human beings we learn through our senses. The sacraments Christ instituted work the same way. They employ physical matter but provide supernatural (and natural) benefits. They are the ordinary means Christ uses to extend salvation to the whole world.

Sacraments are "an outward sign instituted by Christ to give grace." Signs are visible symbols of things that are invisible. Sacraments are efficacious signs helping to bring about the very reality they signify. They do what they symbolize.

While all seven sacraments of the Church are the actions of Christ, they are not new to the story of salvation history. God has always dealt with humanity in a sacramental manner. The "sacraments" of the Old Testament were not sacraments of grace as we now have in the New Covenant, but foreshadowings of them.

We call the study of this biblical foreshadowing "typology" (see CCC 123–130). Typology is the study of how God's works in the Old Covenant prefigure what he accomplished through Christ in the New Covenant (CCC 128).

Typology is an important tool for interpreting Scripture because salvation history unfolds in three successive stages: The age of nature, the age of law, and the age of grace. Since sacraments were essential to Christ's saving work in the age of grace, they were part of God's plan "from the beginning."

The sacraments established by Christ in the age of grace raise all that was sacramental in the ages of nature and law (see CCC 1151 and Jn 1:14–17). Because of Christ's divine power, the New Covenant sacraments are fewer, less complicated, and more powerful. They are avenues of real grace from which we receive the ability to live as children of God.

What We'll Cover in Lesson Two

PROFILES IN GRACE

Edith Stein, St. Benedicta of the Cross

THEMES COVERED

- How we literally become children of God
- The movement from the visible to the invisible through mystagogy
- What it means to say that Word leads to sacrament
- The intimate relationship between liturgy and the sacraments
- The crucial role of covenants
- Why the sacraments are sacred covenant oaths

SCRIPTURE VERSES READ BY CARDINAL DONALD WUERL IN THIS LESSON

- Galatians 4:4–7
- Genesis 8:20
- Genesis 15:10–12, 17
- Luke 22:14–20
- 2 Corinthians 6:18

"The sacraments of the Church were instituted... to perfect man in things pertaining to the worship of God . . . and to be a remedy against the defects caused by sin. And in either way it is becoming that there should be seven sacraments."

— St. Thomas Aquinas —

Notes

_____

_____

_____

_____

_____

_____

_____

_____

_____

_____

_____

_____

_____

_____

_____

_____

_____

_____

_____

"Understanding . . . consists of showing why there are a number of covenants with mankind and in teaching what is the character of those covenants."

— St. Irenaeus —

Review Questions

1. What is the main purpose of a covenant and how were they made in the Old Testament?

2. What is the Latin word for "oath"? How do we swear covenants now?

3. What is "Mystagogy"?

Discussion Questions

1. Why is a personal relationship with God important, but not enough? What kind of relationship does God really desire?

2. What does the kind of relationship God wants to have with us tell us about the kind of relationships he wants us to have with others? How can the sacraments help us in our relationships with others?

3. After these first two lessons, has your understanding of the sacraments changed?

4. Why is it important to cooperate with the graces given in the sacraments?

THIS LESSON'S MEMORY VERSE

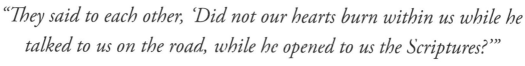

"They said to each other, 'Did not our hearts burn within us while he talked to us on the road, while he opened to us the Scriptures?'"
~ *Luke 24:32* ~

FOLLOW-UP READING AND PREPARATION FOR THE NEXT LESSON

&❧ *Swear to God* by Scott Hahn, pp. 26–37

&❧ *Speaking the Love of God* by Jacob Wood, pp. 17–36

&❧ *Catechism of the Catholic Church*, paragraphs 1213–1284

Additional study resources can be found at www.StPaulCenter.com

Lesson Three
The WATERS of SALVATION

"Holy Baptism is the basis of the whole Christian life, the gateway to life in the Spirit (*vitae spiritualis ianua*), and the door which gives access to the other sacraments."

— *CCC 1213*

Review of the Previous Lesson

Because God revealed himself as Father, the idea of God's family is very important—even in the Old Testament. But in the New Covenant we become part of the family of God in a way that was never possible in the Old Testament (Jn 1:12). Through the sacraments of the New Covenant we actually participate in the divine nature of God (2 Pt 1:4)—we really become his children (Gal 4:4–7).

And once incorporated into his Mystical Body, Christ makes power available to us through the sacraments to crucify our old passions and manifest the fruit of the Spirit. Through the sacraments we can live as true children of our loving Father.

St. Paul shows us that the sacraments lead us into the mystery of Christ (CCC 1075, see 2 Cor 4:18). This process is called "mystagogy." Mystagogy literally means "doctrine of the mysteries." Essentially, it is typology applied to the sacraments. Just as the events of the Old Testament have many levels of meaning and fulfillment in light of Jesus, the rites of the Church do as well.

We encounter the sacraments in the liturgy. Scripture, sacraments, and liturgy are made for each other. They are most at home when they are together. Word leads to sacrament in the liturgy. The liturgy announces the Scriptures and then actualizes them through the sacraments.

The liturgy we celebrate in the New Covenant is a continuation and fulfillment of the liturgies celebrated in the Old Covenant. Time after time we read about altars and sacrifice. That's because it is natural for man to worship God in a liturgical manner.

We meet Christ as we celebrate the sacraments in the liturgy. The sacraments continue the acts of God of the Old and New Testaments. Jesus fulfills the sacrificial liturgy of the Old Testament and gives us the model in Luke 24 (the road to Emmaus) for how to celebrate the New Covenant liturgy.

Having their foundation in Christ, the sacraments are divine actions. However, Christ entrusted them to the Church and made his priests "stewards of the mysteries of God" (1 Cor 4:1). Though priests have been given the authority to celebrate the sacraments, it is by the power of Christ alone that every sacrament produces its effects: The valid celebration of the sacraments does not depend upon the abilities or holiness of the individual priest.

The sacraments are not some type of magic trick by which we can manipulate God. Christ established the sacraments so as to offer us graces, and in order to receive them we need to be disposed to live them.

More than a personal relationship, God wants to make us a part of his family. That happens through covenants, which are not the same thing as contracts. A covenant is a permanent exchange of persons. It creates a family. Covenants are made by an oath sworn in God's name.

Sacrements of inetiation

We swear to God and God, in effect, swears to us.

In Latin, the word for "oath" is *sacramentum*. Through the sacraments we swear a covenant oath with God and are incorporated into his family. The seven Sacraments of Baptism, Confirmation, the Eucharist, Matrimony, Holy Orders, Penance, and Anointing of the Sick are now the means through which we swear our covenant oath to God.

🕊 What We'll Cover in Lesson Three

PROFILES IN GRACE
Bernard Nathanson

THEMES COVERED

- How Baptism joins us to the Mystical Body of Christ
- Why Baptism is necessary, but merely the first step toward salvation
- Why we're still subject to the effects of the Original Sin of Adam and Eve
- The Old Testament foreshadowings of Baptism
- Why the Church baptizes infants
- How Christ fulfills all the Old Testament types of Baptism

SCRIPTURE VERSES READ BY CARDINAL DONALD WUERL IN THIS LESSON

- Acts 8:35–40
- Romans 6:3–4
- 1 Peter 3:18–22
- 1 Corinthians 10:1–4
- Acts 2:37–42

"Baptism is God's most beautiful and magnificent gift. . . . We call it gift, grace, anointing, enlightenment, garment of immortality, bath of rebirth, seal, and most precious gift. It is called gift because it is conferred on those who bring nothing of their own; grace since it is given even to the guilty."

— *St. Gregory* —
of Nazianzus

Notes

_____

_____

_____

_____

_____

_____

_____

_____

_____

_____

_____

_____

_____

_____

_____

_____

_____

_____

_____

_____

_____

_____

_____

"All the baptized must announce Jesus with our life, with our witness, and with our words."

— Pope Francis —

Review Questions

1. What are the three Sacraments of Initiation?

   Baptism, Confirmation, Eucharist

2. Does Baptism guarantee salvation? Why or why not?

3. What are the consequences of Original Sin?

4. Why is Baptism so important?

5. What are three Old Testament "types" of Baptism?

   Circumcism

   Walk thru Jordan River

Discussion Questions

1. What does St. Paul mean when he writes, "Work out your salvation with fear and trembling" in Philippians 2:12?

_____

2. Why was it necessary for Christ to be baptized in the Jordan?

_____

THIS LESSON'S MEMORY VERSE

"And Peter said to them, 'Repent, and be baptized every one of you in the name of Jesus Christ for the forgiveness of your sins; and you shall receive the gift of the Holy Spirit.'"
~ *Acts 2:38* ~

FOLLOW-UP READING AND PREPARATION FOR THE NEXT LESSON

✻ *Swear to God* by Scott Hahn, pp. 40–57

✻ *Speaking the Love of God* by Jacob Wood, pp. 37–53

✻ *Catechism of the Catholic Church*, paragraphs 1285–1321

Additional study resources can be found at www.StPaulCenter.com

Lesson Four
On a MISSION from GOD

"The Spirit of the Lord is upon me, because he has anointed me to preach good news to the poor. He has sent me to proclaim release to the captives and recovering of sight of the blind, to set at liberty those who are oppressed, to proclaim the acceptable year of the Lord."

Luke 4:18–19

Review of the Previous Lesson

In his encounter with the two disciples on the road to Emmaus, Christ showed us the pattern that we still follow today as we celebrate the sacraments. In Acts 8, we see another example of this same movement of Word leading to sacrament, when the deacon Phillip explains the Scriptures to an Ethiopian eunuch and then baptizes him (Acts 8:35–40).

Baptism is "the basis of the whole Christian life, the gateway to life in the Spirit, and the door which gives access to the other sacraments" (CCC 1213).

For this reason, Baptism is the necessary first step in the process of salvation for those who have heard the Gospel and have the opportunity for the sacrament (Jn 3:5b). Baptism, however, does not guarantee salvation. Rather, it is the beginning of justification and the moment where the Holy Spirit gives us sanctifying grace so that we can grow in virtue, belief, and love of God.

While Baptism is the necessary first step, the grace we receive through the sacrament has to unfold and grow. St. Paul exhorted the Church at Philippi to "work out your own salvation with fear and trembling" (Phil 2:12). Ultimately, God is the one who determines salvation. And while "God has bound salvation to the sacrament of Baptism . . . he himself is not bound by his sacraments" (CCC 1257).

Because of the original sin of Adam and Eve, we still suffer sin's effects. Suffering, illness, death, and other frailties of life remain. We also have what we call concupiscence, a general inclination to sin.

Though we continue to suffer the ill effects of sin, we aren't totally corrupt. The graces contained in the sacraments of the New Covenant help restore proper order. Just as Adam passed on to us the effects of original sin, the New Adam passes on to us the graces that are the result of his life, death, and Resurrection (Rom 5:12, 17–18).

When Jesus was baptized, he instituted the Sacrament of Baptism. His Baptism blessed and sanctified the waters, thus making the sacrament efficacious. Christ later tells his disciples to "go therefore and make disciples of all nations, baptizing them in the name of the Father and of the Son and of the Holy Spirit" (Mt 28:19).

As the disciples follow Jesus' instructions we see the same pattern we saw at both Emmaus and in the story of Philip and the Ethiopian—Word leading to sacrament. This continued at Pentecost. The proclamation of the Word illuminated by Christ led to the celebration of the sacrament (Acts 2: 37–42). This continues in the liturgy—the ritual public worship of God's covenant family. Word leads to sacrament in the liturgy.

☙ What We'll Cover in Lesson Four

PROFILES IN GRACE

Cardinal Henry Manning

THEMES COVERED

- ❧ Old Testament prefigurements of Baptism in the Easter Vigil liturgy
- ❧ Confirmation as a share in the mission of the Messiah
- ❧ Oil as the sign of Confirmation
- ❧ How we're anointed to be priests, prophets, and kings

SCRIPTURE VERSES READ BY CARDINAL DONALD WUERL IN THIS LESSON

- ❧ Luke 3:22–23

"Recall then that you have received the spiritual seal, the spirit of wisdom and understanding, the spirit of right judgment and courage, the spirit of knowledge and reverence, the spirit of holy fear in God's presence. Guard what you have received. God the Father has marked you with his sign; Christ the Lord has confirmed you and has placed his pledge, the Spirit, in your hearts."

— St. Ambrose —

Notes

Christ = anmointedone

"We can study the whole history of salvation, we can study the whole of Theology, but without the Spirit we cannot understand. It is the Spirit that makes us realize the truth or—in the words of Our Lord—it is the Spirit that makes us know the voice of Jesus."

— Pope Francis —

Review Questions

1. When did the disciples receive the fullness of the Spirit? What effect did it have on them?

2. What does Confirmation give to us?

3. While Baptism makes us sons and daughters of God, what is the role of Confirmation?

4. Who confers Confirmation in the Latin Rite?

Discussion Questions

1. How should the graces of Confirmation impact the way we live our lives as Christians?

2. Can you think of an instance when you experienced one or more of the gifts of the Holy Spirit in a concrete way?

THIS LESSON'S MEMORY VERSE

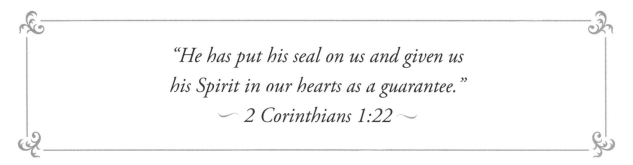

"He has put his seal on us and given us
his Spirit in our hearts as a guarantee."
— *2 Corinthians 1:22* —

PREPARATION FOR NEXT LESSON

- *Swear to God* by Scott Hahn, pp. 60–87
- *Speaking the Love of God* by Jacob Wood, pp. 55–65
- *Catechism of the Catholic Church*, paragraphs 1322–1355

Additional study resources can be found at www.StPaulCenter.com

Lesson Five
The SACRIFICIAL OFFERING

"Then they told what had happened on the road, and how he was known to them in the breaking of the bread."

— Luke 24:35

Review of the Previous Lesson

Baptism is made manifest through the Church by the power of the Spirit. The same Spirit that anointed Christ in the Jordan River at the institution of the sacrament continues his work through his bride. The water of Baptism restores the grace lost through Original Sin and grants new birth as a child of God (Jn 1:12–13).

Confirmation is the second of the Sacraments of Initiation, completing and perfecting the grace first received at Baptism (CCC 1285). It roots us "more deeply in the divine filiation" (CCC 1316). In other words, it helps us grow as sons and daughters of God.

We're anointed after our Baptism because we're following Christ's example. Jesus was anointed by the Spirit following his Baptism. The Fathers of the Church saw Christ's anointing by the Spirit after he came out of the water as corresponding to the anointing received by Israelite kings and priests when they were installed in office. Like others who had preceded him, once anointed, Jesus was now in a sense formally invested with the messianic office.

Whereas Baptism brought us into the family and fully made us sons and daughters, Confirmation outfits us for our mission. Christ's work has become our work. Baptism made us sons of God, but our goal is to be just like Christ. And he wasn't only Son. He was also Messiah. That is what we are called to be as well.

Confirmation is conferred by the bishop or a priest through the laying on of hands and an anointing with perfumed oil, called "chrism." "Chrism" is derived from the same word as "Christ." In Greek, "Christ" means "anointed one." When we are anointed with chrism, we become "christs."

At Pentecost, the grace of the Holy Spirit was made available to all. Having been confirmed, the disciples become bold, preaching the good news of Christ through the power of the Spirit. Scripture also shows us that the disciples transmitted the anointing they received through the imposition of hands (Acts 8:17, 19:6).

When Christ was anointed by the Spirit in the New Testament, he fulfilled in himself the roles of the priests, prophets, and kings of the Old Testament. In fact, Jesus specifically identifies himself as the anointed one of God. Through the Sacrament of Confirmation his anointing is extended to us. Just as he was sealed with the Holy Spirit, "he has put his seal on us and given us his Spirit in our hearts as a guarantee" (2 Cor 1:22).

What We'll Cover in Lesson Five

PROFILES IN GRACE

Alfred Hitchcock

THEMES COVERED

- The Eucharist as "source and summit of our Christian life"
- The Emmaus Road encounter as a template for the Mass
- The pattern of sacrifice seen throughout salvation history
- Old Testament roots of the Eucharistic sacrifice

SCRIPTURE VERSES READ BY CARDINAL DONALD WUERL IN THIS LESSON

- Hebrews 6:4–5
- Hebrews 7:15–17
- Genesis 22:7–8

"I have no taste for corruptible food nor for the pleasures of this life. I desire the bread of God, which is the flesh of Jesus Christ, who was of the seed of David; and for drink I desire his blood, which is love incorruptible."

— *St. Ignatius* —
of Antioch

Notes

_____

_____

_____

_____

_____

_____

_____

_____

_____

_____

_____

_____

_____

_____

_____

_____

_____

_____

_____

"Since Christ himself said, 'This is my body',
who shall dare to doubt that it is His body?"

— St. Cyril of Jerusalem —

Review Questions

1. How is Jesus' priesthood similar to Melchizedek's priesthood?

2. What are the similarities between Abraham's sacrifice of Isaac and Christ's sacrifice on the Cross?

Discussion Questions

1. Has a deeper understanding of the Old Testament roots of the Eucharist changed your view of the sacrament?

2. How can a deeper understanding of the Scriptures help us to enter more deeply into the mystery of the Eucharist?

THIS LESSON'S MEMORY VERSE

"Those who received his word were baptized . . . and they devoted themselves to the apostles' teaching and fellowship, to the breaking of bread and the prayers."
— *Acts 2:41–42* —

PREPARATION FOR NEXT LESSON

- *Swear to God* by Scott Hahn, pp. 90–97
- *Speaking the Love of God* by Jacob Wood, pp. 65–72
- *Catechism of the Catholic Church*, paragraphs 1356–1390

Additional study resources can be found at www.StPaulCenter.com

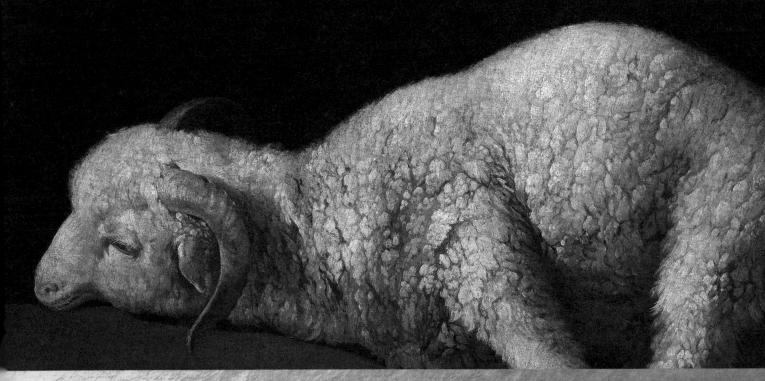

Lesson Six
LAMB *of* GOD

> "I am the living bread which came down from heaven; if any one eats of this bread, he will live for ever; and the bread which I shall give for the life of the world is my flesh."
>
> *John 6:51*

Review of the Previous Lesson

The Eucharist completes our initiation as Christians. The Catechism tells us "the Eucharist is 'the source and summit of the Christian life'" (1324). It is also where we give thanks to God for all he has done for us. The Greek word *eucharistia* means "thanksgiving."

Just like at Emmaus (Lk 24), Christ is present and made known to us in the two parts of the Mass, even though we cannot see him. The liturgy of the Word leads to, and is fulfilled in, the liturgy of the Eucharist.

This pattern is also present in the earliest evidence we have of early Church life outside of the Bible. In AD 155, St. Justin Martyr testified to this in a letter to the emperor regarding the Masses of the early Christians. What we do in the Mass has deep roots in the Old Testament. In fact, Peter said that the precious blood of Christ offered as an unblemished lamb was part of God's plan from before "the foundation of the world" (1 Pet 1:19–20). We see this especially in the Bible's depictions of Melchizedek, Abraham, and the Passover.

Following a military victory by Abraham, Melchizedek "king of Salem brought out bread and wine; he was priest of God Most High" (Gen 14:18). He blesses Abraham and then receives a tithe from him.

Abraham's sacrifice of Isaac also illuminates Christ's sacrifice. Jesus and Isaac were both the "only beloved" sons of their fathers. They both carried the wood themselves for their sacrifice. Both sacrifices took place on a Jerusalem hill. Calvary, the site of Jesus' sacrifice, was a hill in Moriah's range. And since the journey to Moriah took three days, both fathers received their sons back on the third day. Matthew identifies Jesus as "the son of Abraham" (Mt 1:1) Abraham even prophesies about the sacrifice of Christ on the Cross (Gen 22:8).

St. Paul also tells us in Galatians that God sacrifices himself so "that in Christ Jesus the blessing of Abraham might come upon the Gentiles, that we might receive the promise of the Spirit through faith" (Gal 3:14).

☙ What We'll Cover in Lesson Six

PROFILES IN GRACE
J.R.R. Tolkien

THEMES COVERED

- ❧ The role of the ten plagues in the sacrificial history of Israel

- ❧ The importance of the Passover sacrifice as a "redemption"

- ❧ Why Jesus is called the "Lamb of God"

- ❧ The famous Eucharistic passage of John 6 and Christ's Real Presence

- ❧ Parallels between the Passover sacrifice and the crucifixion of Christ

- ❧ How the Mass is a re-presentation of the once-and-for-all sacrifice of Christ

SCRIPTURE VERSES READ BY CARDINAL DONALD WUERL IN THIS LESSON

- ❧ John 6:51

- ❧ John 6:53–56

- ❧ 1 Corinthians 5:7–8

"Because this bread and wine have been made Eucharist, we call this food Eucharist, and no one may take part in it unless he believes that what we teach is true, has received baptism for the forgiveness of sins and new birth, and lives in keeping with what Christ taught."

— St. Justin Martyr —

Notes

_____

_____

_____

_____

_____

_____

_____

_____

_____

_____

_____

_____

_____

_____

_____

_____

_____

_____

_____

_____

"It would be easier for the world to survive without the sun than to do without the holy Mass."

— St. Padre Pio —

Review Questions

1. What were the Israelites commanded to do in order to fulfill the requirements of the original Passover sacrifice in the book of Exodus?

2. In John 6 what does Jesus declare himself to be and why does he use such graphic language?

3. How does John show us that Christ is the Lamb of the new Passover?

4. What is the response to non-Catholics who accuse the Church of "re-sacrificing" Christ at every Mass?

5. Why was Christ's sacrifice more effective than all the sacrifices of the Israelites?

Discussion Questions

1. Given what we've learned so far, how central should the Mass be in our lives?

2. What does Christ's sacrifice on the Cross say about his love for us?

THIS LESSON'S MEMORY VERSE

"Truly, truly, I say to you, unless you eat the flesh of the Son of man and drink his blood, you have no life in you."
~ *John 6:53* ~

PREPARATION FOR NEXT LESSON

- *Swear to God* by Scott Hahn, pp. 100–115
- *Speaking the Love of God* by Jacob Wood, pp. 72–81
- *Catechism of the Catholic Church*, paragraphs 1391–1419

Additional study resources can be found at www.StPaulCenter.com

Lesson Seven
HEAVEN *on* EARTH

"By the Eucharistic celebration we already unite ourselves with the heavenly liturgy and anticipate eternal life, when God will be all in all."

CCC 1326

Review of the Previous Lesson

Christ is a high priest and king like Melchizedek. But he is also the sacrificial offering itself. The Passover illuminates this truth. During their 430 years in Egypt, the Israelites had begun worshiping the Egyptian gods. God wanted this to end. Pharaoh refused to free the Israelites from their captivity, so in nine horrific plagues God proceeded to figuratively slay the gods of the Egyptians.

Preceding the final plague, in which the angel of death would kill all firstborn sons and livestock, God gave the Israelites a means of salvation. So that the death angel would "pass over" their houses leaving the firstborn unharmed, each Israelite family had to take an unblemished lamb without broken bones, kill it, sprinkle its blood on the doorway, and eat the lamb that same night. The sacrificial lamb was offered as a ransom in place of their firstborn. After their deliverance, they were to reenact this sacrifice every year. This Old Testament sacrifice of the Passover was a precursor of Christ's sacrifice. That's why Christ was called the "Lamb of God."

The feeding of the five thousand in John 6 sheds further light on this. The event itself takes place during the Passover. Jesus told the crowd that he was the new Passover lamb. Just like the Passover lamb, Jesus was saying that he had to be eaten. Jesus was not speaking figuratively. He used graphic language so the crowd would know his language wasn't symbolic.

One year later, Jesus' trial takes place in the context of the Passover. Throughout its description of the events leading up to it, and the crucifixion itself, John's Gospel draws parallels between Jesus and the Passover lamb and links him to the high priest.

John tells us that Jesus' trial took place at the same time the priests began to slaughter the Passover lambs (19:14). He says that none of Christ's bones were broken (Jn 19:36). He was served sour wine from a sponge on a hyssop branch, the same type of branch used for sprinkling the blood of the lamb on the doorpost at Passover (Ex 12:22). The seamless tunic Jesus was wearing at his crucifixion was the same as the vestments worn by the high priest when he offered sacrifice (Jn 19:23–24, Lev 16:4; 21:10). This was to imply that Christ acted as High Priest when he made himself a sacrifice on the Cross.

In telling us that Christ is both Lamb and Priest, John mimics what Jesus did. At the Last Supper Jesus uses priestly language and describes himself as a sacrificial Victim.

In taking up and fulfilling the sacrificial history of Israel, the Lamb of God accomplished what the blood of millions of slain animals could not. For the salvation of the world a sacrifice as good and perfect as God himself was necessary. This was the purpose of the Cross. The animal sacrifices leading up to Christ served as preparation for the true Lamb of God. Jesus bore the curses of all sin and failure and offered a New Covenant with his own blood.

Scripture makes it clear that the sacrifice of Christ was a one-time event (Heb 7:27; 10:12).

Rather than a re-sacrifice, the Eucharist is the re-presentation of the Paschal sacrifice of Jesus Christ. Jesus told his disciples "Do this in remembrance of me" (Lk 22:19; 1 Cor 11:25). The Greek word for "remembrance" is *anamnesis* (AN-AM´-NAY-SIS). *Anamnesis* is not simply recalling a past event: It is "the making present of a past event."

As it journeyed beyond the time of Christ and the disciples, the Church demonstrated its understanding of the ritual and doctrine of the Eucharist. There are many examples displaying the overwhelming consensus of the Church with regard to the Eucharist. It has always been understood to be the Body, Blood, Soul and Divinity of our Lord Jesus Christ re-presented to us in the Mass.

☺ What We'll Cover in Lesson Seven

PROFILES IN GRACE

Alec Guinness

THEMES COVERED

⁂ How Old Testament worship reflected the heavenly worship

⁂ How New Covenant liturgy is heaven on earth

⁂ The connection between the Book of Revelation and the Mass

⁂ Why the Eucharist is a *parousia*

⁂ The Church as the Kingdom of God

SCRIPTURE VERSES READ BY CARDINAL DONALD WUERL IN THIS LESSON

⁂ Hebrews 12:22–24

⁂ Revelation 19:9–10

⁂ Revelation 5:6

⁂ Matthew 24:34–35

⁂ Luke 22:15–18

"With the Eucharist, therefore, heaven comes down to earth, the tomorrow of God descends into the present and it is as if time remains embraced by divine eternity."

— *Pope Benedict XVI* —

Notes

"*There is nothing so great as the Eucharist. If God had something more precious He would have given it to us.*"

— *St. John Vianney* —

Review Questions

1. How did the ancient Israelites understand the relationship between the earthly temple and the heavenly Temple? Between the earthly liturgy and the heavenly liturgy?

2. How has that relationship changed since the coming of Christ?

3. What are some of the similarities drawn between the earthly liturgy and the heavenly liturgy in the Book of Revelation?

4. When does Christ come again?

5. What is the Kingdom of God on earth?

Discussion Questions

1. Has this new approach to reading John's Apocalypse (the Book of Revelation) changed your view on this book?

2. Discuss some practical ways to overcome distractions at Mass.

THIS LESSON'S MEMORY VERSE

> *"And the angel said to me, 'Write this: Blessed are those who are invited to the marriage supper of the Lamb.' And he said to me, 'These are true words of God.'"*
> — *Revelation 9:9–10* —

PREPARATION FOR NEXT LESSON

- *Swear to God* by Scott Hahn, pp. 118–127
- *Speaking the Love of God* by Jacob Wood, pp. 85–107
- *Catechism of the Catholic Church*, paragraphs 1420–1470

Additional study resources can be found at www.StPaulCenter.com

Lesson Eight
RECONCILED *to* GOD

"Peace be with you. As the Father has sent me, even so I send you.' And when he had said this, he breathed on them, and said to them, 'Receive the Holy Spirit. If you forgive the sins of any, they are forgiven; if you retain the sins of any, they are retained.'"

John 20:21–23

Review of the Previous Lesson

At Mount Sinai God gave Moses detailed instructions on how to construct the tabernacle that would serve as the place of worship for the Israelites, where God would "dwell in their midst." The Israelites understood that the buildings were created to enable an imitation of heavenly worship. Their liturgy reflected the heavenly liturgy. This is attested to by the Old Testament prophets.

Even so, the Israelites understood that heaven and earth remained separate. With the Incarnation of Jesus Christ, this changed. By assuming the flesh of man, Christ brought heaven to earth and joined the two forever in the most intimate way. In his very flesh, he perfected and fulfilled the ancient Israelite worship. He is both Priest and Victim.

Through the sacraments, we are joined to Christ—we are part of his Body—and he has taken us back to heaven with him. Now instead of just imitating angelic worship, through the New Covenant liturgy, we worship with the angels. Since we now participate in the heavenly liturgy together, there is no more need for earthly imitations (Heb 12). The Old Testament shows us the initial pattern of Israel's liturgical worship. The New Testament illustrates its fulfillment. In the Book of Revelation, we see the new nature of our worship. There, liturgy is the key to understanding what St. John has to say.

In reading Revelation in light of the Mass, we see obvious liturgical language. John worships on Sunday. He is told by one resembling a high priest in vestments to record what he sees. There are references to altars and incense; the Eucharist; the "Holy, Holy, Holy" (i.e. the *Sanctus*); and a great multitude in heaven cries out, "Alleluia." Revelation also illuminates the new relationship of God and his people, showing men and angels worshipping together around the throne of God. In former times, only the Israelite high priest was allowed into the inner chamber of the tabernacle or temple—God's dwelling place.

In Revelation, the Church is shown as a kingdom of priests who freely enter the "Holy of Holies" in the heavenly Temple. Jesus is our new High Priest in the Holy of Holies of the heavenly Temple. Through the sacraments he established, we now have the ability to become what he always wanted us to be—a kingdom of priests serving and worshiping in the courts of heaven. This is what happens when we celebrate the Mass.

This union of heaven and earth is consummated in the Eucharist. John picks up on a theme used by St. Paul. In Ephesians 5, Paul describes the Church as the bride of Christ. In Revelation, that bride is unveiled. In the Eucharist, we become one with the Body of Christ and participate in the marriage supper of the Lamb (Rev 19:9).

The sacrifice of Jesus on the Cross took place within the context of the Israelite feast of Passover. Jesus is the perfect Passover Lamb who was slain for the sins of the world. Accordingly, the Lamb of God is at the center of the liturgy in Revelation.

Christ's coming isn't just a future event. It is already happening in the liturgy. At Mass, Christ is truly made present to us. The Eucharist is the *parousia*.

The glory of Christ in the Eucharist is veiled when his Body and Blood come to us in the form of bread and wine. In the same manner the glory of Christ's kingdom is veiled. It comes to us in the form of a Church populated by imperfect humans. But while we long for God's perfect kingdom to be fully revealed at the end of time, we need to realize that even now the kingdom Christ spoke of is here.

What We'll Cover in Lesson Eight

PROFILES IN GRACE

Rudolf Höss

THEMES COVERED

- The parable of the Prodigal Son as a story of restoration
- The call of Christ to perfection
- Original Sin and consequences of the Fall
- Penitential rituals in the Old Testament
- Internal and external healing by Christ in the New Testament
- The disciples' authority to forgive sins through Christ

SCRIPTURE VERSES READ BY CARDINAL DONALD WUERL IN THIS LESSON

- Genesis 3:8
- Leviticus 5:5–6
- Nehemiah 9:1–2
- Mark 2:5–11

"Those who approach the sacrament of Penance obtain pardon from God's mercy for the offense committed against him, and are, at the same time, reconciled with the Church which they have wounded by their sins and which by charity, by example, and by prayer labors for their conversion."

— *Lumen Gentium* —
11, 2

Notes

_____
_____
_____
_____
_____
_____
_____
_____
_____
_____
_____
_____
_____
_____
_____
_____
_____
_____
_____
_____
_____

*"Confession is an act of honesty and courage—
an act of entrusting ourselves, beyond sin, to the
mercy of a loving and forgiving God."*

— *Pope St. John Paul II* —

Review Questions

1. What is the origin of our struggle with sin?

2. What was God looking for from Adam and Eve when he questioned them in the Garden?

3. How were sins forgiven in ancient Israel?

4. What did the physical healings performed by Jesus signify?

5. Why do we confess our sins to a priest?

Discussion Questions

1. In what ways do our attitudes towards our own sins resemble those of Adam, Eve, and their children?

2. How can venial sin do as much damage as mortal sin?

3. What are the advantages of going to Confession regularly?

THIS LESSON'S MEMORY VERSE

"Create in me a clean heart, O God, and put a new and right spirit within me. Cast me not away from thy presence, and take not thy Holy Spirit from me. Restore to me the joy of thy salvation, and uphold me with a willing spirit."
~ *Psalm 51:10–12* ~

PREPARATION FOR NEXT LESSON

- *Swear to God* by Scott Hahn, pp. 130–152
- *Speaking the Love of God* by Jacob Wood, pp. 109–124
- *Catechism of the Catholic Church*, paragraphs 1480–1535

Additional study resources can be found at www.StPaulCenter.com

Lesson Nine
SPIRITUAL HEALING

"He was wounded for our transgressions, he was bruised for our iniquities; upon him was the chastisement that made us whole, and with his stripes we are healed."

— *Isaiah 53:5*

Review of the Previous Lesson

Penance is a Sacrament of Healing because it helps us overcome the weakness towards sin that remains even after Baptism. This inclination to sin often damages our spiritual life. We all suffer from this defect.

In spite of our weaknesses, we are called to "be perfect as your heavenly Father is perfect" (Mt 5:48). The Sacrament of Penance is an important way he gives us that power.

God desires a covenant relationship with humanity. Sin disrupted our communion with God, but his covenant with humanity has always provided a way to restore the relationship. Confession, penance, and reconciliation are nothing new. This is seen right from the beginning of salvation history.

Immediately after they sinned, God gave Adam and Eve the opportunity to confess. Instead, neither took responsibility or expressed sorrow for their actions. This cycle continued with Adam and Eve's son Cain.

But God didn't tire of seeking confession and reconciliation. He kept the path to relationship with his people wide open, as we have seen in Leviticus 5:5–6. In penitential rituals, God insists on a confession and then gives the sinner a liturgical act of sacrifice and penance. All of this was accomplished through the intercession of a priest.

Israel's rites for confession, sacrifice, and penance were very difficult. Yet even with the sacrificial and sacramental acts of penance they performed, the Israelites continued to fall into sin. As difficult and complicated as they were, their offerings could not make up for their offenses.

The sacrifices and confessions of the Israelites didn't force God to forgive them. He forgave out of love for his people, just as he does today. Forgiveness was his divine right, and his alone.

Jesus forgave people's sins and physically healed them to signify their spiritual healing. Then Christ passed on his divine right to the disciples. By sharing his life with these first priests of the New Covenant, he gave them the power to administer sacraments. The Church now shared God's power through the incarnate Christ.

This idea of a priestly class exercising authority with regard to sin was not new to salvation history since it had been in place in the Old Testament. As they receive their authority through their ordination, sharing in the new priesthood of Christ, our clergy can forgive our sins. This is why we go to them for confession. We don't confess to a priest instead of Christ. Rather, Christ the High Priest acts through the human priest to whom we confess.

Sin ruptures our communion with God and our communion with his Church. That's why the Catechism tells us that "conversion entails both God's forgiveness and reconciliation with the Church" (1440).

What We'll Cover in Lesson Nine

PROFILES IN GRACE

Fr. Emil Kapaun

THEMES COVERED

- The difference between mortal and venial sin
- The connection between Penance and the rest of the sacraments
- A true understanding of God's mercy
- The primary purpose of Anointing of the Sick
- Old Testament roots of the Anointing of the Sick
- Redemptive suffering

SCRIPTURE VERSES READ BY CARDINAL DONALD WUERL IN THIS LESSON

- Psalm 103:2–3
- Matthew 14:13–14
- James 5:14–16

"By the sacred anointing of the sick and the prayer of the priests the whole Church commends those who are ill to the suffering and glorified Lord, that he may raise them up and save them. And indeed she exhorts them to contribute to the good of the People of God by freely uniting themselves to the Passion and death of Christ."

— *Lumen Gentium 11* —

Notes

_____

_____

_____

_____

_____

_____

_____

_____

_____

_____

_____

_____

_____

_____

_____

_____

_____

_____

_____

"And in this is fulfilled also what St. James the Apostle says: if any one is sick, let him call in the priests of the Church, and let them lay hands on him, anointing him with oil in the name of the Lord, and the prayer of faith shall save the sick man, and if he be in sins they shall be remitted to him."

— *Origen* —

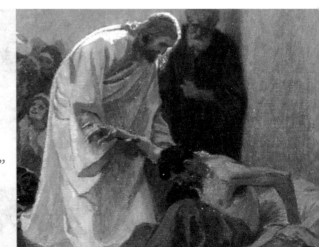

Review Questions

1. What is the primary purpose of Anointing of the Sick?

2. Where in Scripture do we see this sacrament instituted?

3. To whom does James say we should go when we're sick?

4. What does James mean by "elder"?

Discussion Questions

1. What should our attitude towards suffering be?

2. How can our physical sufferings help us, those we love, and the whole Church?

3. Have you ever witnessed any physical or spiritual healing from this sacrament?

THIS LESSON'S MEMORY VERSE

"Is any among you sick? Let him call for the elders of the church, and let them pray over him, anointing him with oil in the name of the Lord; and the prayer of faith will save the sick man, and the Lord will raise him up; and if he has committed sins, he will be forgiven."
~ *James 5:14–15* ~

PREPARATION FOR NEXT LESSON

❧ *Swear to God* by Scott Hahn, pp. 154–180

❧ *Speaking the Love of God* by Jacob Wood, pp. 127–128, 147–172

❧ *Catechism of the Catholic Church*, paragraphs 1533–1535, 1601–1666

Additional study resources can be found at www.StPaulCenter.com

Lesson Ten
BRIDES *and* BRIDEGROOMS

"Scripture speaks throughout of marriage and its 'mystery,' its institution and the meaning God has given it, its origin and its end, its various realizations throughout the history of salvation, the difficulties arising from sin and its renewal 'in the Lord' in the New Covenant of Christ and the Church."

CCC 1602

Review of the Previous Lesson

Though the details differ from the Old Covenant, the essential elements of the New Covenant version of penance remains the same. For our part, we need to be truly sorry, state our sorrow by naming our sins, and fulfill the penance or restitution assigned by our priest-confessor. We call it "our work," but in a sense it is all the work of the Holy Spirit as he urges us on to conversion (CCC 1448).

While the Church only requires us to make a good confession of serious sin once a year, we should go more often because mortal sin destroys our spiritual life. Venial sins also damage our spiritual life, causing spiritual illness. Penance is a Sacrament of Healing—restoring the life of the spirit and our communion with God.

Frequent confession is directly connected to the other sacraments, especially the Eucharist. St. Paul warned the Christians in Corinth: "Whoever, therefore, eats the bread or drinks the cup of the Lord in an unworthy manner will be guilty of profaning the body and blood of the Lord. . . . That is why many of you are weak and ill, and some have died" (1 Cor 11:27, 30).

The second Sacrament of Healing is the Anointing of the Sick. Any grave illness or impending physical danger, such as a serious operation, warrants its use. Administered by the priest through the anointing of oil, this sacrament strengthens against temptation to discouragement in the face of serious illness or death.

Anointing of the Sick is not primarily concerned with bodily health, but with spiritual healing. It is preparation for the final journey to our Father's house. However, we still always pray for physical healing secure in the knowledge our Father will grant it as long as it helps us toward salvation (CCC 1512).

The Church draws its understanding of the Anointing of the Sick from Scripture where we see the connection between spiritual and physical health relate to one another (e.g. Num 21:5–9 and Jn 3:14–15).

The New Testament is full of stories of Christ, and subsequently his disciples, healing people's afflictions. But while he compassionately cured the physical ailments of many, he didn't heal everyone.

He came to earth to deal with the root of our problem—sin. And in so doing, He gave new meaning to the consequences of sin because he used those consequences—suffering and death—to redeem and save us. He transformed and elevated all human suffering.

Incorporated into his Body through the sacraments, our suffering can be united to his, and become part of the plan of redemption. We can use our afflictions to help the Body of Christ. Anointed with the oil of this healing sacrament, we receive the courage to endure and the grace to offer up our sufferings along with Christ.

The Anointing of the Sick is alluded to in Mark 6:13 when the disciples "anointed with oil many who were sick and healed them." James 5 tells us that when we're sick we're to call for the "elders." "Elders" is a literal translation of the Greek word *presbyteros*—the root word from which we get the English word "priest." In other words, we don't just go to anyone when we're really sick. Just as in Penance, we go to a priest.

What We'll Cover in Lesson Ten

PROFILES IN GRACE

Dolores Hope

THEMES COVERED

- The nuptial nature of creation
- God as a family of persons
- Marriage as the primordial sacrament in creation
- Marriage as an icon of God's love throughout Scripture
- The marriage of Christ to the Church and the New Covenant sacrament

SCRIPTURE VERSES READ BY CARDINAL DONALD WUERL IN THIS LESSON

- Exodus 31:16–17
- Genesis 1:26–27
- Genesis 2:21–23
- Hosea 2:19–21

"Marriage is an act of the will that signifies and involves a mutual gift, which unites the spouses and binds them to their eventual souls, with whom they make up a sole family —a domestic church."

— *Pope St. John Paul II* —

Notes

_____
_____
_____
_____
_____
_____
_____
_____
_____
_____
_____
_____
_____
_____
_____
_____
_____
_____

*"When husband and wife are united in marriage
they no longer seem like something earthly, but
rather like the image of God Himself."*

— *St. John Chrysostom* —

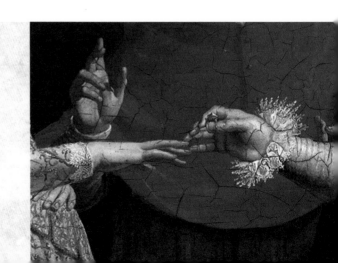

Review Questions

1. How does the author of Genesis show us that a wedding is taking place in the Creation account?

2. Who does John want us to see Jesus as in his account of the Wedding at Cana? How?

Discussion Questions

1. How does God's love for his bride, the New Israel, show us about the way we are called to love our spouses?

2. What can cause our marriages to be less than a perfect imitation of the Trinity?

THIS LESSON'S MEMORY VERSE

" So they are no longer two but one. What therefore God has joined together, let not man put asunder."
⁓ *Matthew 19:6* ⁓

PREPARATION FOR NEXT LESSON

❧ *Swear to God* by Scott Hahn, pp. 182–200

❧ *Speaking the Love of God* by Jacob Wood, pp. 129–146, 173–175

❧ *Catechism of the Catholic Church*, paragraphs 1536–1600

Additional study resources can be found at www.StPaulCenter.com

Lesson Eleven
ORDAINED *to* SERVE

"The Lord has sworn and will not change his mind, 'You are a priest for ever after the order of Melchiz'edek'."

— *Psalm 110:4*

Review of the Previous Lesson

The creation narrative in Genesis tells us that in the beginning there was a wedding of grace and nature. It was a marriage between Creator and creation. Created in God's "image and likeness," man and woman were made to be in a unique covenant relationship with God and each other. God created man as a family because God is family.

In marriage, we imitate the family life of the Trinity through loving self-donation. The Father, Son, and Holy Spirit give of themselves completely to each other. In so doing they form a perfect family of persons. In the same manner, male and female come together in covenant relationship and fully give of themselves to each other.

Since it is an ancient Hebrew text, Scripture doesn't describe the wedding of our first parents in modern terms. In describing Eve as "bone of my bones and flesh of my flesh," Adam uses family covenant language echoed elsewhere in Scripture.

Marriage is a recurring theme in Scripture used to show God's desire to wed himself to his people. Scripture uses nuptial imagery because it perfectly portrays the covenant relationship with his people that God has been after from the beginning. From creation on, marriage was to be a sign of the love between God and his people.

The importance of marriage to the message of Jesus is underscored by the fact that he performed his first miracle at a wedding. John shows that Jesus is the true Bridegroom, and that God is fulfilling his promise to come as a divine Bridegroom to Israel. Jesus gave his own life for the life of the Church. He married her, indissolubly and forever. This is what makes matrimony a New Covenant sacrament. The husband and wife are the ministers of this sacrament, though a priest or deacon ordinarily "witnesses" the event for validity. While freely given vows ratify a marriage covenant, this sacrament becomes indissoluble—permanent until death—when the two become one through sexual intercourse.

Imaging the relationship between Christ and his Church means that our marriages are meant to be fruitful. That's why the Church forbids anything that would inhibit matrimony's power to be a sign of Christ's love for his beloved. This would include divorce, polygamy, birth control, and abortion, among other things.

To help couples image the nuptial union of Christ and the Church, married couples receive an increase in sanctifying grace specially given to those who enter this sacrament. In addition to a closer relationship with our spouse, we are joined more closely to Christ.

What We'll Cover in Lesson Eleven

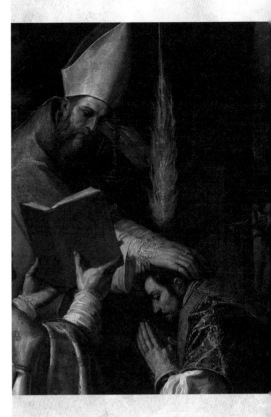

PROFILES IN GRACE

Fr. Miguel Pro, S.J.

THEMES COVERED

- The common priesthood and the ministerial priesthood
- The priesthood of Adam and the role of the first-born son
- How the Levitical priesthood came into existence at Mount Sinai
- David as priest-king and the transition toward the New Covenant
- The restoration and transformation of the priesthood in Jesus Christ
- Apostolic Succession and the nuptial symbolism of a male priesthood

SCRIPTURE VERSES READ BY CARDINAL DONALD WUERL IN THIS LESSON

- Exodus 32:26–29
- Hebrews 5:1–6

"O Priest! You are not yourself because you are God. You are not of yourself because you are the servant and minister of Christ. You are not your own because you are the spouse of the Church. You are not yourself because you are the mediator between God and man. You are not from yourself because you are nothing. What then are you? Nothing and everything."

— St. Norbert —

Notes

"The power of the priest, is the power of the divine person; for the transubstantiation of the bread requires as much power as the creation of the world."

— *St. Bernardine of Siena* —

Review Questions

1. In the New Covenant, what are the two types of priesthood? How do they differ?

2. Why do we know Jesus was setting up a new priesthood to replace the Levitical priesthood?

Discussion Questions

1. What does it mean for us to call our priests and bishops "father"?

2. What does the priesthood tell us about the life we hope to live in heaven?

THIS LESSON'S MEMORY VERSE

"The Lord has sworn and will not change his mind, 'You are a priest for ever after the order of Melchizedek.'"
~ *Psalm 110:4* ~

Additional study resources can be found at www.StPaulCenter.com

Lesson Eleven Review Notes

Through the Sacraments of Baptism and Confirmation, all Christians share in the priesthood of Christ, but there are two types of priesthoods in the Church: the common priesthood of the baptized and the ministerial priesthood.

Through the Sacrament of Holy Orders, the ministerial priesthood is composed of ordained bishops and priests. Its role is to serve the common priesthood. Deacons, the third degree of the Sacrament of Holy Orders, are ordained to the service of the ministerial priesthood and the laity.

In ancient biblical times, fathers acted as priests for their families. This priesthood was then passed down from the father to his first-born son. Examples are seen in Adam, Noah, Abraham, Isaac, and Jacob, and Melchizedek.

When the Israelites were unfaithful at the foot of Mount Sinai, they lost the corporate vocation to be a nation of priests. The Levites became the ministerial priesthood.

As the High Priest of the New Covenant, Christ fulfilled and finally ended the role of the Levitical priesthood. At the Last Supper, he instituted a new sacrament—Holy Orders. As members of his priesthood, the Apostles were commanded to "Do this in remembrance of me." After his Resurrection, Christ gave power to his twelve disciples to continue his work of forgiving sins, healing the sick, casting out demons, and other sacred duties.

In Matthew 16:19, Jesus appoints Peter as the leader of the twelve disciples—the first pope. The office was permanent, but its power would be given to another when Peter died. In Acts chapter 1, Matthias replaces Judas as one of the Twelve. This is the first example of the passing on of apostolic authority, commonly referred to as Apostolic Succession. All bishops can trace their lineage back to the Apostles.

Christ never uses the word "priest" when he established his disciples as such. By the actions he took he made it perfectly clear he was fulfilling and replacing the Old Covenant priesthood. We see this in the way he set up his priesthood, mimicking Moses.

Priesthood is not a right; it is a calling that comes only from God. A vocation is an invitation to give of oneself completely to another in accordance with the divine plan. Jesus chose men as his priests and for this reason the Church can only ordain males.

Our priests are icons of Christ. They are natural, perceptible signs that act in the same manner as other sacramental signs. Our priests image the incarnated Jesus Christ, who was, and remains, a man. Also, Christ is the true Bridegroom who gives of himself to his bride, the Church, in the marriage supper of the Lamb. A male priest is naturally symbolic of this role as the bridegroom.

This idea in no way devalues the role of women. Does not the Blessed Virgin Mary surpass all the

Apostles in dignity and excellence? Yet she was not invested with the apostolic ministry.

We all have our role. We must remember the priesthood is a calling. It is a sacrifice of love.

In Matthew 22, Christ says that we will no longer be given in marriage in heaven. Marriage is an imitation of Trinitarian life. But in heaven, we actually participate in what we imitated on earth. This is one reason priests are not married in the Latin Rite. Through celibacy, a priest's relationship with Christ foreshadows our ultimate reality—nuptial union with the Most Holy Trinity.

Appendix
Common Prayers

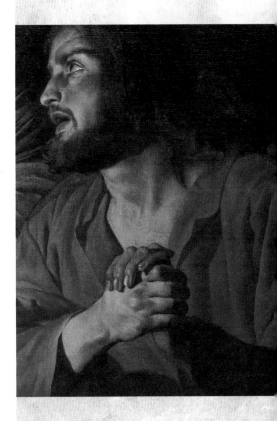

OUR FATHER

Our Father, Who art in heaven,
Hallowed be Thy Name.
Thy Kingdom come.
Thy Will be done, on earth as it is in heaven.
Give us this day our daily bread.
And forgive us our trespasses,
as we forgive those who trespass against us.
And lead us not into temptation,
but deliver us from evil.
Amen.

HAIL MARY

Hail Mary,
Full of Grace,
The Lord is with thee.
Blessed art thou among women,
and blessed is the fruit
of thy womb, Jesus.
Holy Mary,
Mother of God,
pray for us sinners now,
and at the hour of death.
Amen.

COME HOLY SPIRIT

Come, Holy Spirit, fill the hearts of Thy faithful and
enkindle in them the fire of Thy love.
V. Send forth Thy Spirit and they shall be created.
R. And Thou shalt renew the face of the earth.
Let us pray. O God, Who didst instruct the hearts of the
faithful by the light of the Holy Spirit, grant us the same
Spirit to be truly wise, and ever rejoice in his consolation.
Through Christ our Lord.
Amen.

GLORY BE

Glory be to the Father,
and to the Son,
and to the Holy Spirit.
As it was in the beginning,
is now,
and ever shall be;
world without end.
Amen.

ANIMA CHRISTI

Soul of Christ, sanctify me
Body of Christ, save me
Blood of Christ, inebriate me
Water from Christ's side, wash me
Passion of Christ, strengthen me
O good Jesus, hear me
Within Thy wounds hide me
Suffer me not to be separated from Thee
From the malicious enemy defend me
In the hour of my death call me
And bid me come unto Thee
That I may praise Thee with Thy saints
and with Thy angels
Forever and ever
Amen.